Specimen Sight-Reading Tests for Clarinet

Grades 1–5

ABRSM

MIX
Paper from responsible sources
FSC
www.fsc.org FSC™ C109619

GRADE 1

Moderato

1

Allegro moderato

2

Allegretto

3

© 1995 by The Associated Board of the Royal Schools of Music AB 2468

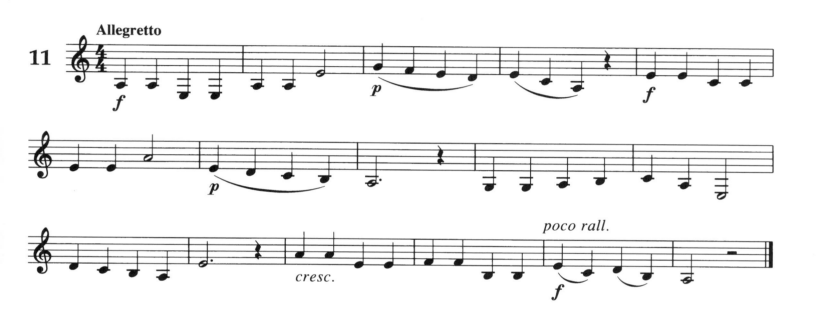

GRADE 2

5 Allegro giocoso

6 Larghetto

7 Moderato

GRADE 3

4 Andante con moto

5 Allegretto

6 Alla gavotta

GRADE 4

GRADE 5

Typeset by Musonix
Printed by Caligraving Limited, Thetford, Norfolk, England

AB 2468

9:12